INVITATIONS
TO LITERACY

PRESE... EARTH PATROL PROTECT

D1407532

Acknowledgements appear on page 226.

Printed in the U.S.A.

ISBN: 0-395-73554-8

123456789-VH-98 97 96 95 94

Houghton Mifflin Company • Boston
Atlanta • Dallas • Geneva, Illinois • Palo Alto • Princeton

PRESERVE AND PROTECT
EARTH PATROL

CONTENTS

FRAGILE: HANDLE WITH CARE

PAPERBACK **PLUS**™

A River Ran Wild

by Lynne Cherry

How did a dead river in Massachusetts come back to life?

In the same book . . .

More about how pollution can ruin a river and how concerned people can help save it.

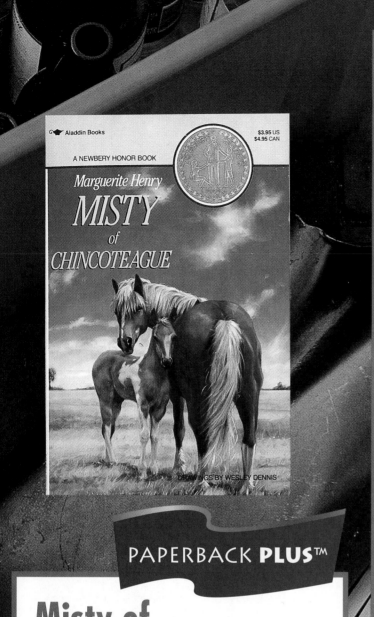

More Earth Books

Someday a Tree
by Eve Bunting
After someone dumps chemicals that poison her favorite oak tree, Alice plants an acorn nearby, hoping that another tree will start to grow.

Sato and the Elephants
by Juanita Havill
A Japanese ivory carver becomes a stone carver instead, when he finds out that elephants are killed to supply him with ivory.

Earth Keepers
by Joan Anderson and George Ancona
This three-part photo essay describes a community garden in New York, Lynn Rogers's work with black bears, and the environmental studies done by the crew of the *Clearwater*.

Alligators: A Success Story
by Patricia Lauber
Once an endangered species, the alligator is making a comeback, thanks to caring citizens and new laws.

Listening to Crickets: A Story About Rachel Carson
by Candice F. Ransom
A biography of the writer and biologist whose work helped make people aware of threats to the environment.

PAPERBACK **PLUS**™

Misty of Chincoteague
by Marguerite Henry

Can two children tame the wild mare and her young colt Misty?

In the same book . . .

A lot more about the real Misty, where she lived, and other fun facts about horses.

A SIERRA CLUB BOOK

THE GREAT YELLOWSTONE FIRE

CAROLE G. VOGEL AND KATHRYN A. GOLDNER

IN YELLOWSTONE NATIONAL PARK, heat and water escape from the earth into a land of mystery. Where volcanoes once erupted, strange creations of nature now bubble and hiss. Colorful, steaming pools dot fields of bunchgrass and sagebrush. Geysers gurgle and shoot columns of superheated water high into the air.

Around these simmering landforms rise the rugged Rocky Mountains of Wyoming, Montana, and Idaho. Sharp gray peaks capped with snow tower above green forests. Streams and rivers tumble through deep gorges.

Lodgepole pine trees blanket much of Yellowstone. These trees grow tall and thin with few branches. In the dense forests, their tops mesh together, and little sunlight filters through. Open meadows and groves of spruce, fir, and aspen trees interrupt the pines.

A dramatic fountain of steam and hot water shoots skyward from Castle Geyser, just one of about 10,000 geysers, hot springs, and other thermal features in Yellowstone.

Yellowstone's patchwork of habitats provides homes for many kinds of animals. Near steaming geysers and hot springs, bison graze in open meadows. Moose and deer browse on tender shoots of cottonwood and willow. On steep mountainsides, golden eagles build nests on rocky ledges, and bighorn sheep traverse the jagged rocks. The rivers and lakes of the park provide food and nesting sites for trumpeter swans, white pelicans, and other water birds.

In 1872, the vast area known as Yellowstone was declared a national park to preserve its special landforms, wildlife, and wilderness for future generations to enjoy. The rules of the national park protect the animals from hunters and the trees from loggers. But no one can protect the forests from the forces of nature. As in ages past, summertime brings wildfire to Yellowstone.

In 1886, fourteen years after the formation of the park, Yellowstone officials declared fire the enemy. Although fire had been part of the wilderness for thousands of years, firefighters armed with axes and

An elk and her young calf share a quiet moment by a stream. Seven large herds of elk roam the meadows and forests of Yellowstone.

The variety of animal life in the park is remarkable, ranging from black bears like this little cub (top) to flocks of waterbirds such as the American white pelican (bottom).

shovels were now sent to stamp out blazes. For many years, there was no effective way to combat flames in areas far from roads. After World War II, lookouts were stationed on mountaintops to watch for smoke, and smoke jumpers parachuted from airplanes into hard-to-reach places. Wildfires were extinguished as soon as possible.

Fallen trees, dead pine needles, and other natural litter continued to pile up on the forest floor. As the lodgepole forests aged, pine bark beetles attacked the trees, until thousands of dead and dying pines filled the forests. No major fires cleared away this buildup of fuel.

Over the years, as scientists learned more about forests, they discovered that fire is not the enemy. By clearing the land and releasing the

minerals locked in dead wood, fire creates and maintains a variety of habitats. Like sunshine and rain, fire is necessary to the health of the wilderness.

In 1972, scientists convinced park officials to allow fire to play its role in nature once again. Under the new policy, firefighters battled only blazes started by humans and those natural fires that threatened people or buildings. Precipitation in all seasons kept much of Yellowstone moist, so most natural fires died quickly.

In 1988, park officials expected another normal fire season. After a dry winter, spring precipitation was high. Fires ignited by lightning all fizzled out.

Then, in June, conditions changed. The air turned hot and dry, and practically no rain fell. Day after day, the sun beat down on Yellowstone. Lakes and streams shrank. In the meadows, grasses shriveled. In the forests, dead lodgepole pines and fallen branches became parched. Slowly, the landscape changed from lush green to withered brown.

Thunderstorms rumbled across the park but brought no rain. Lightning ignited many small fires. Some died quickly, while others sprang to life. The fires burned unevenly, scorching here, singeing there. They

In the summer of 1988, lightning started more than forty-five fires in Yellowstone — twice the usual number for one summer.

124

leapfrogged through the forests, leaving patches of trees and ground cover untouched. Pushed along by dry summer winds, the fires grew.

Just over the park boundary in Targhee National Forest, woodcutters accidentally started another fire. The flames quickly spread into Yellowstone. Firefighters battled this blaze and several others that threatened buildings, but they could not stop the fires.

By midsummer, almost 9,000 acres of Yellowstone's 2.2 million acres had burned. Fires raged through forests that had taken hundreds of years to grow. No rain was expected for weeks, and officials were worried. On July 15, they decided to fight all new natural blazes. Within a week, they began to battle all existing ones, as well. Yet the fires continued to spread.

Wildfires usually burn more slowly at night, then rev up with the heat of day. But in the summer of 1988, dry night winds blew down from high ridges, fanning the blazes. Day and night, ground fires crackled through dead pine needles, branches, and logs,

The landscape became a patchwork of colors that reflected the pattern of burn. Scorched brown trees separated the areas blackened by the hottest flames from the green areas left untouched (above). Hot flames leapt up tinder-dry tree trunks (left).

blackening the forest floor. In some places, they scorched the bases of trees but left the tops green. In other areas, the ground fires burned hotter and toasted needles in the crowns of the trees a dusty rust color.

The hottest flames clawed up the trunks of large trees. Treetops ignited in seconds, and smoke poured into the sky. Lodgepole pines burst apart, hurling bits of glowing wood through the air. These tiny blazing embers landed on dry branches or grass and kindled spot fires far ahead of the fire fronts.

Advancing as much as five to ten miles a day, the fires hopscotched through the wilderness. Among the burned forests and meadows, they left unburned areas of green trees and brown grass.

From sunup to sunset and into the night, nearly 9,500 firefighters from all parts of the country battled the blazes. Many of these men and women prepared firebreaks. They cleared strips of ground of everything that could burn. Sometimes they scraped the land with hand tools; at other times, they detonated explosives or set small backfires. They sprayed trees and buildings with water or fire-retardant foam and snuffed out spot fires.

To fight remote blazes, firefighters hiked into the backcountry. Smoke

Firefighters tried every known technique to control the blazes. On the roads, fire engines often shared the smoky landscape with animals trying to keep out of the fire's way (above). In the roadless wilderness, planes dropped pink fire retardant to smother the flames (left).

jumpers parachuted in. Sometimes fire crews dropped water or fire retardant onto the blazes from helicopters and airplanes.

Yet the fires defied everyone's best efforts. Blazes subdued by water or retardant leapt back to life. Small fires grew and joined with bigger fires. Flames skipped over prepared firebreaks, roads, and rivers. One blaze even jumped the Grand Canyon of the Yellowstone River. By mid-August, experts agreed that only a change in weather could stop the fires.

But the forecast for hot, dry weather remained

unchanged. On August 20, the day that would be called Black Saturday, gale-force winds fanned every blaze in the park. Flames rampaged through forests and meadows. Smoke billowed high into the sky, and gray ash rained down.

Powerless, firefighters could only stand and watch while fire consumed another 160,000 acres. More of Yellowstone was blackened on this one day than in the previous 116 years. The amount of burned area in the park had doubled.

In late summer, fires inside and outside Yellowstone whipped toward several towns neighboring the park. Flames threatened many buildings inside Yellowstone, as well. Weary firefighters battled the blazes for twelve to fourteen hours a day.

Despite the raging fires, many people refused to cancel their vacations. They came to see the smoke, the wildlife, and the world's most famous geyser, Old Faithful.

Close to Old Faithful stands the rustic Old Faithful Inn, built in stagecoach days from logs, shingles, and stone. When it was completed in 1904, the inn and a cluster of buildings stood alone amid the geysers. Today, the inn is but one of many buildings—stores, gas stations, other lodges—that make up Old Faithful Village.

During the dry days of early September 1988, fire burned toward the famous geyser and the wooden structures of the nearby village. On the morning of September 7, officials began to evacuate tourists and workers from the area. Most people cooperated, but a few refused to leave.

At 2:00 P.M., the wind gathered speed. Beyond a nearby ridge, flames danced in the treetops. Lodgepole pines pitched and swayed, and the smell of burning trees filled the air. As the blaze swept up the far side of the ridge, fire-engine crews drenched buildings with water or fire-retardant foam. Other firefighters turned on a sprinkler system at the edge of the village complex.

At 3:30, Old Faithful erupted. Minutes later, a wall of flames whipped over the ridge. Roaring like jets in takeoff, the fire rolled down

Fire roared over a ridge in Upper Lamar Valley;

a similar blaze approached Old Faithful.

On September 7, fire whipped down the hillside behind Old Faithful Village. The wind shifted, and suddenly flames headed toward the buildings.

the forested hillside. Trees ignited like torches. Clouds of smoke turned the sky orange . . . then bronze . . . then gray. . . .

Within minutes, fire engulfed a pine grove on the edge of the village. Cabins burst into flames. A truck burned and then exploded.

Park employees, reporters, and the few remaining visitors fled toward the relative safety of the parking lot around Old Faithful Inn. Smoke stung their eyes and throats. Hot coals pelted their backs and flew past their heads.

Fire crews sprayed the buildings as pumper trucks raced through the smoky village to extinguish spot fires. A rooftop sprinkler system flooded the shingles of the inn.

Minutes later, the fire reached the edge of the village. Engulfed in thick smoke and threatened by blazing embers, historic Old Faithful Inn was saved by a rooftop sprinkler system.

For more than an hour, the fire roared and crackled around the village. It jumped a barren stretch of land and continued to burn on the other side. Bypassed by the flames, Old Faithful geyser erupted right on schedule. Its spray mixed with the ash-laden air and drained away, a gray slurry.

When the smoke finally cleared, twenty structures on the outskirts of the village—mostly cabins and storage buildings—lay in smoldering ruins. But Old Faithful Inn and the other major buildings survived unharmed.

For three more days, fires roared through Yellowstone. Then, on September 11, a light snow fell. In the following days, moist fall weather slowed the flames, and the thick smoke began to break up and drift away. Though fires smoldered for many weeks, the major battle was over.

All through the summer, while the forests and meadows were burning, the animals followed their instincts, and most survived. Small meadow animals, such as squirrels and mice, hid from flames in underground burrows. Large mammals, such as bears and elk, seemed to sense the movement of the fires and wandered away.

Once the flames had passed, wildlife quickly returned to the burned sites. Insects fed on charred trees, and birds snapped up the insects. Squirrels and chipmunks scrounged for seeds. Hawks and owls hunted the small animals that had lost their hiding places.

In recently burned areas, elk licked the ash for minerals (left); squirrels and owls searched for food in the charred forest (right). During the summer of 1988, nearly one-half of Yellowstone was touched by flames.

In moist sites, new plant growth soon poked through the blackened earth, but the nourishing green shoots grew too sparsely to feed all the animals. Already lean from grazing on drought-stricken land, deer, bison, and elk could not build up thick fat reserves. They faced a difficult winter.

By late November, heavy snows chilled Yellowstone. The seven previous winters had been mild, and few large mammals had died. Now, bigger-than-normal herds of elk, deer, and bison competed for a smaller-than-normal food supply. Many of these grazing animals began to starve. During storms and cold snaps, hundreds of the very young and the very old died. Their frozen bodies provided food for bears, coyotes, and bald eagles.

Coyotes and other scavenging animals feasted on elk and deer that perished during the harsh winter after the fire.

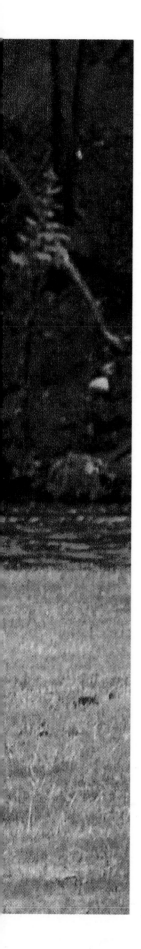

More animals than usual migrated into neighboring forests and towns in search of food. Outside Yellowstone, park rules did not protect the animals. Hunters killed far more elk and bison than in previous years.

In the spring, melting snow moistened the parched ground of Yellowstone. Unharmed roots of blackened grasses and shrubs absorbed the water. Countless seeds that had survived in the soil swelled with moisture. Many other seeds drifted into the burned areas from nearby patches of healthy vegetation. Together with sunlight and the nutrients from burned wood and underbrush, the water triggered an ancient cycle of regrowth.

Grasses sprouted and wildflowers bloomed. Aspens grew new branches and leaves. Berry bushes blossomed and thrived. Freed from their cones by the fires, lodgepole pine seeds germinated. Among the new flowers and grasses, tiny green pine trees dotted the ash.

The elk and bison that survived the harsh winter fattened up on the rich new growth. Bears feasted on berries, and porcupines nibbled fresh, green grass. Squirrels and mice flourished on the abundance of new seeds. Woodpeckers in search of insects pounded holes in dead trees, creating nesting sites for songbirds.

Within a few growing seasons, a carpet of grasses, flowers, shrubs, and tiny tree seedlings will transform most of Yellowstone's burned areas into lush meadows. These new meadows will provide a bounty of food for the animals.

As the bushes and shrubs continue to grow, they will shade the sun-loving plants beneath them. Gradually the grasses and flowers will die. The lodgepole pine seedlings will poke above the other plants; in a decade, they will be three to four feet high.

Eventually wind will knock down most of the blackened trees. Along streams and rivers, the toppled trunks will support the

A bison grazed on tender new grasses, her calf
at her side, as springtime brought renewal to
the park.

banks. They will break up the current and improve the habitat for trout and other fish.

The young pines will grow taller and taller, and within forty years new lodgepole forests will replace the forests that burned. The high branches of the pines will grow together and prevent sunlight from reaching the forest floor. In the dim understory, the bushes and shrubs will die; they will no longer provide berries and shoots for hungry animals. The new dense stand of trees will contain little variety of food. Most animals will move on to new meadows created by more recent fires.

Summer wildfires have been changing the landscape of Yellowstone for at least 12,000 years. Most of the time, fires burn relatively small areas and alter the landscape only slightly. But every 250 to 400 years, a combination of drought, strong winds, and fuel buildup produces colossal wildfires that sweep through the aging lodgepole forests and change the landscape more significantly.

Below the surface of Yellowstone, forces far more powerful than wildfire have been shaping the land for millions of years — the forces of volcanism. Long ago, violent volcanic eruptions helped sculpt the mountains and plateaus of this region. Today, volcanic fires still simmer in the form of hot, melted rock two miles underground. The heat from this rock fuels the park's geysers, fumaroles, mudpots, and hot springs.

Someday far in the future, volcanoes will again erupt at Yellowstone. As in the distant past, these underground fires will alter the pattern of mountains and plateaus.

Much sooner, massive wildfires will again roar through Yellowstone. As in the summer of 1988, these surface fires will spark the renewal of meadows and forests.

Geologic wonders such as Minerva Terrace at Mammoth Hot Springs are the work of volcanic forces even more powerful than wildfire.

Meet the Authors

Carole G. Vogel

Kathryn A. Goldner

In 1981, Carole Vogel and Kathryn Goldner wrote *Why Mount St. Helens Blew Its Top,* and they have been writing together ever since. They have written books for children, science activity books, and magazine articles. What is it like to write a book with another person? Vogel and Goldner say that when they work together, they learn from each other. They also help each other over the rough places.

One of the hard things about working together, however, is being honest with each other. That is especially true when something written by the other person needs more work. Another problem is deciding whose name comes first on the cover. Vogel and Goldner say that they take turns. So — how will their names appear on their next book?

Hot Ideas

Write a Postcard

Before Your Very Eyes

You are one of the tourists at Old Faithful Inn during the Yellowstone fire. How do you feel? Terrified? Excited? Write a postcard describing your feelings and what you see, smell, and hear. Illustrate your message if you wish.

Write a Want Ad

Smokey the Bear Needs Help!

He needs you to write a want ad for a job fighting forest fires in Yellowstone National Park. In the ad, tell what qualities you are looking for in a firefighter, what skills are needed, and what kind of experience would be helpful. Explain why the job is important so that lots of people will apply.

In Tonight's News

Give a series of progress reports about the Yellowstone fire as if you were a television reporter on the evening news. Try to create a sense of danger and suspense so your audience knows what it feels like to be at the scene of the disaster. You might also perform with a partner and be "co-anchors."

Camping Tips

People camping in the wilderness during hot and dry weather might need some tips. Make a pamphlet or poster explaining what conditions are right for a forest fire and how fires get started by nature and by people. List things that campers can do to avoid starting a forest fire accidentally.

Smoke Jumpers

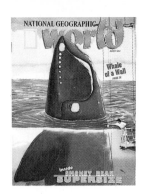

Wherever fires erupt and roads don't go — that's where you'll find smoke jumpers. They parachute into remote mountain wilderness throughout the western United States, including Alaska. Their mission: to prevent small wildfires from growing into large ones. Employed by the Forest Service and the Bureau of Land Management, smoke jumpers have been fighting fires since 1940.

Smoke jumpers land close to a forest fire. They work to prevent the fire from spreading. They rely on obstacles such as rivers, creeks, lakes, and logging roads to help contain the fire. Sometimes they dig a fire line — a dirt path several feet wide through the surrounding vegetation. Their goal is to let the fire burn out while keeping it from reaching the treetops. If it does reach the treetops, there is no way to put out the fire from the ground. A plane carrying fire retardant might be called in to help.

Once the fire is out, smoke jumpers watch for smoke and feel chunks of timber. They must make sure that no areas are still hot. They call this part of their job mopping up.

Smoke jumpers spend sleepless nights listening to a forest fire roaring in the distance. They breathe thick smoke, work up a terrible sweat, and get covered by dirt and ash. At the end of a mission, smoke jumpers have aching bodies. They may face a 20-mile hike to get home. Smoke jumpers have a dangerous but vital job — they save millions of acres of forestland every year.

By Janice Koch

Rocky Touchdown
A mountain slope presents a challenge to a smoke jumper. This one landed face down. Knowing how to land on different kinds of terrain — thick forests, steep hills, lakes — is an essential smoke jumper skill.

All Geared Up and Ready to Go

Smoke jumper Margarita Phillips is well suited to fight a fire. Smoke jumpers put together and repair their own gear — except for their boots and helmets. The equipment Phillips jumps with weighs 85 pounds.

MAIN PARACHUTE
Within five seconds of leaving the plane, a smoke jumper's parachute opens. It is carried inside a backpack.

RESERVE CHUTE
If the main parachute does not open, the reserve chute gets pulled into service.

HELMET
A motorcycle helmet has a protective metal face guard.

JUMPSUIT
The heavily padded jumpsuit is made of the same material as bulletproof vests worn by police officers. Smoke jumpers wear fire-resistant clothing underneath.

LEG POCKETS
Inside go candy bars, long johns, and the "bird's nest" — looped nylon strap (shown on top of the pack-out bag) that smoke jumpers use to descend if they land in a tree.

PACK-OUT BAG
Tucked away in a jumpsuit, this bag is empty at first. Most fire fighting equipment is dropped to the ground in a separate container. Once a fire is out, a smoke jumper puts the equipment in the bag so it can be carried out.

Native American

Keepers of the Earth

The native people of North America speak of their relationship to the Earth in terms of family. The Earth is not something to be bought and sold, something to be used and mistreated. It is, quite simply, the source of our lives — our Mother. And the rest of Creation, all around us, shares in that family relationship. The Okanagan people of the Pacific Northwest speak of the Earth as Mother, the Sun as Father and the animals as our brothers and sisters. This view of the world was held by the Navajo and the Abenaki, the Sioux and the Anishinabe and most of the aboriginal people of this continent. They saw their role on this Earth not as rulers of creation, but as beings entrusted with a very special mission — to maintain the natural balance, to take care of our Mother, to be Keepers of the Earth.

Stories

told by Joseph Bruchac

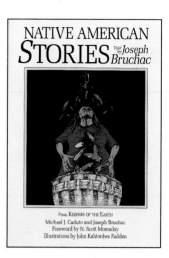

NATIVE AMERICAN
STORIES Told by Joseph Bruchac

From KEEPERS OF THE EARTH
Michael J. Caduto and Joseph Bruchac
Foreword by N. Scott Momaday
Illustrations by John Kahionhes Fadden

Birdfoot's Grampa

The old man
must have stopped our car
two dozen times to climb out
and gather into his hands
the small toads blinded
by our lights and leaping,
live drops of rain.

The rain was falling,
a mist about his white hair
and I kept saying
you can't save them all,
accept it, get back in
we've got places to go.

But, leathery hands full
of wet brown life,
knee deep in the summer
roadside grass,
he just smiled and said
they have places to go to
too.

Gluscabi and the Wind

an Abenaki legend

Long ago, Gluscabi lived with his grandmother, Woodchuck, in a small lodge beside the big water.

One day Gluscabi was walking around when he looked out and saw some ducks in the bay.

"I think it is time to go hunt some ducks," he said. So he took his bow and arrows and got into his canoe. He began to paddle out into the bay and as he paddled he sang:

> Ki yo wah ji neh
> yo ho hey ho
> Ki yo wah ji neh
> Ki yo wah ji neh.

But a wind came up and it turned his canoe and blew him back to shore. Once again Gluscabi began to paddle out and this time he sang his song a little harder:

148

Eagle

KI YO WAH JI NEH
YO HO HEY HO
KI YO WAH JI NEH
KI YO WAH JI NEH.

But again the wind came and blew him back to shore. Four times he tried to paddle out into the bay and four times he failed. He was not happy. He went back to the lodge of his grandmother and walked right in, even though there was a stick leaning across the door, which meant that the person inside was doing some work and did not want to be disturbed.

"Grandmother," Gluscabi said, "what makes the wind blow?"

Grandmother Woodchuck looked up from her work. "Gluscabi," she said, "why do you want to know?"

Then Gluscabi answered her just as every child in the world does when they are asked such a question.

"Because," he said.

Grandmother Woodchuck looked at him. "Ah, Gluscabi," she said. "Whenever you ask such questions I feel there is going to be trouble. And perhaps I should not tell you. But I know that you are so stubborn you will never stop asking until I answer you. So I shall tell you. Far from here, on top of the tallest mountain, a great bird stands. This bird is named Wuchowsen, and when he flaps his wings he makes the wind blow."

"Eh-hey, Grandmother," said Gluscabi, "I see. Now how would one find that place where the Wind Eagle stands?"

Again Grandmother Woodchuck looked at Gluscabi. "Ah, Gluscabi," she said, "once again I feel that perhaps I should not tell you. But I know that you are very stubborn and would never stop asking. So, I shall tell you. If you walk always facing the wind you will come to the place where Wuchowsen stands."

"Thank you, Grandmother," said Gluscabi. He stepped out of the lodge and faced into the wind and began to walk.

He walked across the fields and through the woods and the wind blew hard. He walked through the valleys and into the hills and the wind blew harder still. He came to the foothills and began to climb and the wind still blew harder. Now the foothills were becoming mountains and the wind was very strong. Soon there were no longer any trees and the wind was very, very strong. The wind was so strong that it blew off Gluscabi's moccasins. But he was very stubborn and he kept on walking, leaning into the wind. Now the wind was so strong that it blew off his shirt, but he kept on walking. Now the wind was so strong that it blew off all his clothes and he was naked, but he still kept walking. Now the wind was so strong that it blew off his hair, but Gluscabi still kept walking, facing into the wind. The wind was so strong that it blew off his eyebrows, but still he continued to walk. Now the wind was so strong that he could hardly stand. He had to pull himself along by grabbing hold of the boulders. But there, on the peak ahead of him, he could see a great bird slowly flapping its wings. It was Wuchowsen, the Wind Eagle.

Gluscabi took a deep breath. "GRAND-FATHER!" he shouted.

The Wind Eagle stopped flapping his wings and looked around. "Who calls me Grandfather?" he said.

Gluscabi stood up. "It's me, Grandfather. I just came up here to tell you that you do a very good job making the wind blow."

The Wind Eagle puffed out his chest with pride. "You mean like this?" he said and flapped his wings even harder. The wind which he made was so strong that it lifted Gluscabi right off his feet, and he would have been blown right off the mountain had he not reached out and grabbed a boulder again.

"GRANDFATHER!!!" Gluscabi shouted again.

The Wind Eagle stopped flapping his wings. "Yesss?" he said.

Gluscabi stood up and came closer to Wuchowsen.

151

"You do a very good job of making the wind blow, Grandfather. This is so. But it seems to me that you could do an even better job if you were on that peak over there."

The Wind Eagle looked toward the other peak. "That may be so," he said, "but how would I get from here to there?"

Gluscabi smiled. "Grandfather," he said, "I will carry you. Wait here." Then Gluscabi ran back down the mountain until he came to a big basswood tree. He stripped off the outer bark and from the inner bark he braided a strong carrying strap which he took back up the mountain to the Wind Eagle. "Here, Grandfather," he said. "Let me wrap this around you so I can lift you more easily." Then he wrapped the carrying strap so tightly around Wuchowsen that his wings were pulled in to his sides and he could hardly breathe. "Now, Grandfather," Gluscabi said, picking the Wind Eagle up, "I will take you to a better place." He began to walk toward the other peak, but as he walked he came to a place where there was a large crevice, and as he stepped over it he let go of the carrying strap and the Wind Eagle slid down into the crevice, upside down, and was stuck.

152

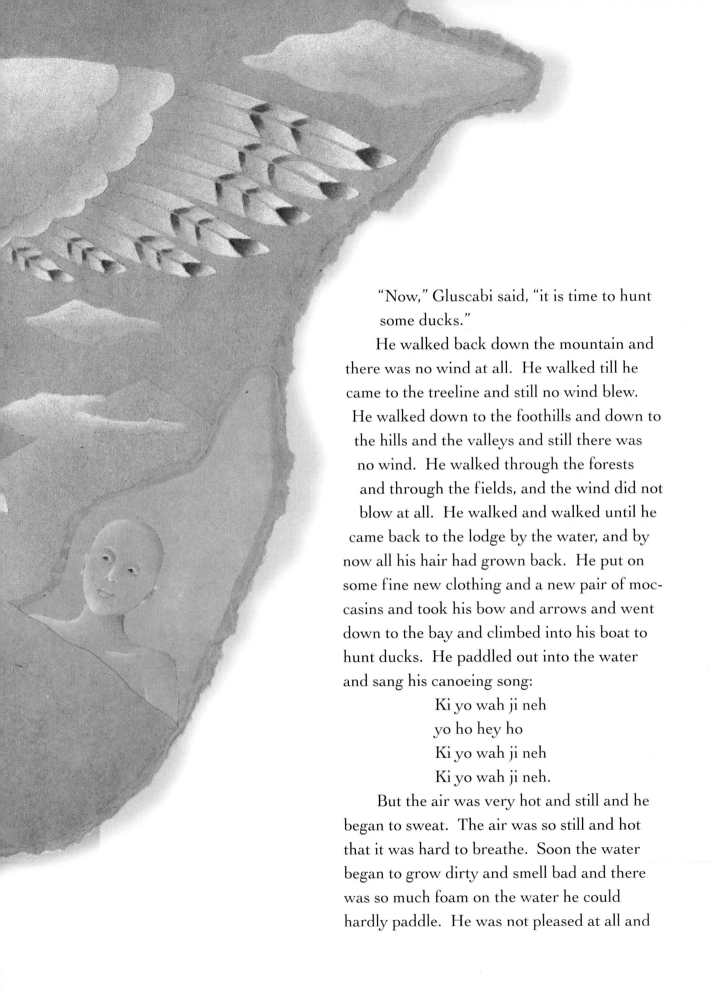

"Now," Gluscabi said, "it is time to hunt some ducks."

He walked back down the mountain and there was no wind at all. He walked till he came to the treeline and still no wind blew. He walked down to the foothills and down to the hills and the valleys and still there was no wind. He walked through the forests and through the fields, and the wind did not blow at all. He walked and walked until he came back to the lodge by the water, and by now all his hair had grown back. He put on some fine new clothing and a new pair of moccasins and took his bow and arrows and went down to the bay and climbed into his boat to hunt ducks. He paddled out into the water and sang his canoeing song:

>Ki yo wah ji neh
>yo ho hey ho
>Ki yo wah ji neh
>Ki yo wah ji neh.

But the air was very hot and still and he began to sweat. The air was so still and hot that it was hard to breathe. Soon the water began to grow dirty and smell bad and there was so much foam on the water he could hardly paddle. He was not pleased at all and

153

he returned to the shore and went straight to his grandmother's lodge and walked in.

"Grandmother," he said, "what is wrong? The air is hot and still and it is making me sweat and it is hard to breathe. The water is dirty and covered with foam. I cannot hunt ducks at all like this."

Grandmother Woodchuck looked up at Gluscabi. "Gluscabi," she said, "what have you done now?"

And Gluscabi answered just as every child in the world answers when asked that question. "Oh, nothing," he said.

"Gluscabi," said Grandmother Woodchuck again, "tell me what you have done."

Then Gluscabi told her about going to visit the Wind Eagle and what he had done to stop the wind.

"Oh, Gluscabi," said Grandmother Woodchuck, "will you never learn? Tabaldak, The Owner, set the Wind Eagle on that mountain to make the wind because we need the wind. The wind keeps the air cool and clean. The wind brings the clouds which give us rain to wash the Earth. The wind moves the waters and keeps them fresh and sweet. Without the wind, life

will not be good for us, for our
children or our children's children."

Gluscabi nodded his head. "Kaamoji,
Grandmother," he said. "I understand."

Then he went outside. He faced in the direction from
which the wind had once come and began to walk. He walked
through the fields and through the forests and the wind did not
blow and he felt very hot. He walked through the valleys and up
the hills and there was no wind and it was hard for him to
breathe. He came to the foothills and began to climb and he was
very hot and sweaty indeed. At last he came to the mountain
where the Wind Eagle once stood and he went and looked down
into the crevice. There was Wuchowsen, the Wind Eagle,
wedged upside down.

"Uncle?" Gluscabi called.

The Wind Eagle looked up as best he could. "Who calls me
Uncle?" he said.

"It is Gluscabi, Uncle. I'm up here. But what are you doing
down there?"

"Oh, Gluscabi," said the Wind Eagle, "a very ugly naked man
with no hair told me that he would take me to the other peak so that
I could do a better job of making the wind blow. He tied my wings
and picked me up, but as he stepped over this crevice he dropped
me in and I am stuck. And I am not comfortable here at all."

"Ah, Grandfath . . . er, Uncle, I will get you out."

Then Gluscabi climbed down into the crevice. He pulled the
Wind Eagle free and placed him back on his mountain and untied
his wings.

"Uncle," Gluscabi said, "it is good that the wind should blow
sometimes and other times it is good that it should be still."

The Wind Eagle looked at Gluscabi and then nodded his head.
"Grandson," he said, "I hear what you say."

So it is that sometimes there is wind and sometimes it
is still to this very day. And so the story goes.

People throw away...
MUCH TOO MUCH

In one year, people in the United States throw away enough trash to fill a bumper-to-bumper line of garbage trucks reaching halfway to the moon.

Every year, forty million acres of tropical rain forest are destroyed worldwide. That's an area larger than the state of California.

156

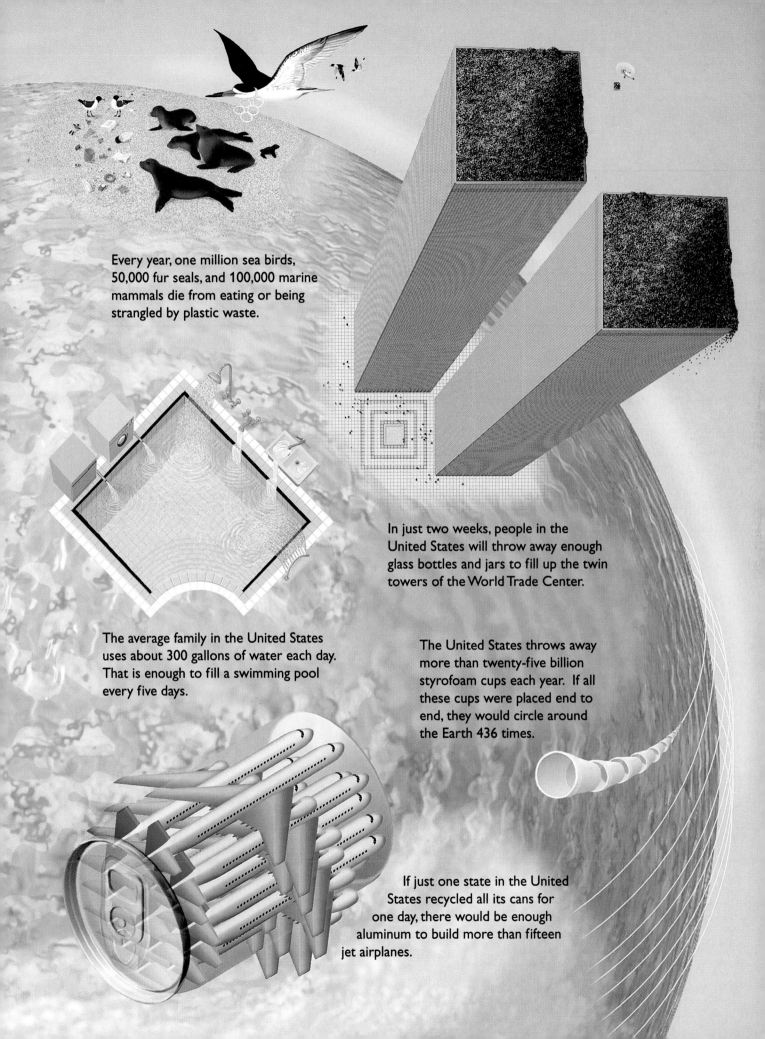

Every year, one million sea birds, 50,000 fur seals, and 100,000 marine mammals die from eating or being strangled by plastic waste.

In just two weeks, people in the United States will throw away enough glass bottles and jars to fill up the twin towers of the World Trade Center.

The average family in the United States uses about 300 gallons of water each day. That is enough to fill a swimming pool every five days.

The United States throws away more than twenty-five billion styrofoam cups each year. If all these cups were placed end to end, they would circle around the Earth 436 times.

If just one state in the United States recycled all its cans for one day, there would be enough aluminum to build more than fifteen jet airplanes.

We Are Plooters

by Jack Prelutsky

illustrated by Paul O. Zelinsky

We are Plooters,
We don't care,
We make messes
Everywhere,
We strip forests
Bare of trees,
We dump garbage
In the seas.

    We are Plooters,
    We enjoy
    Finding beauty
    To destroy,
    We intrude
    Where creatures thrive,
    Soon there's little
    Left alive.

        Underwater,
        Underground,
        Nothing's safe
        When we're around,
        We spew poisons
        In the air,
        We are Plooters,
        We don't care.

159

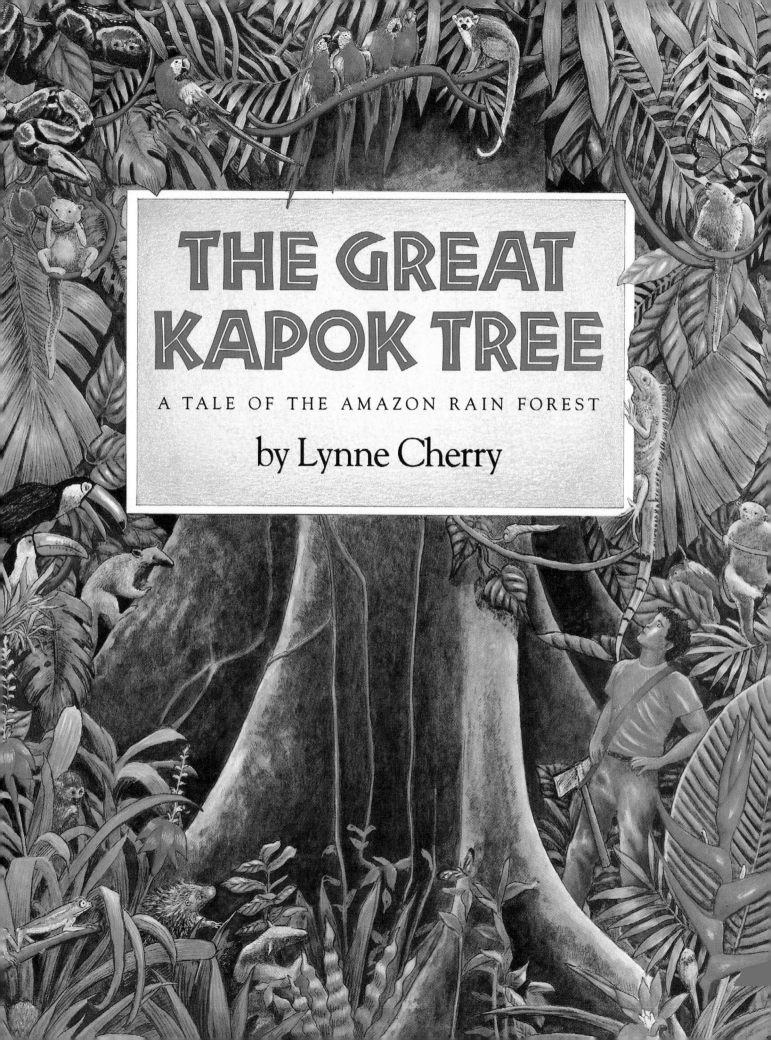

THE GREAT KAPOK TREE

A TALE OF THE AMAZON RAIN FOREST

by Lynne Cherry

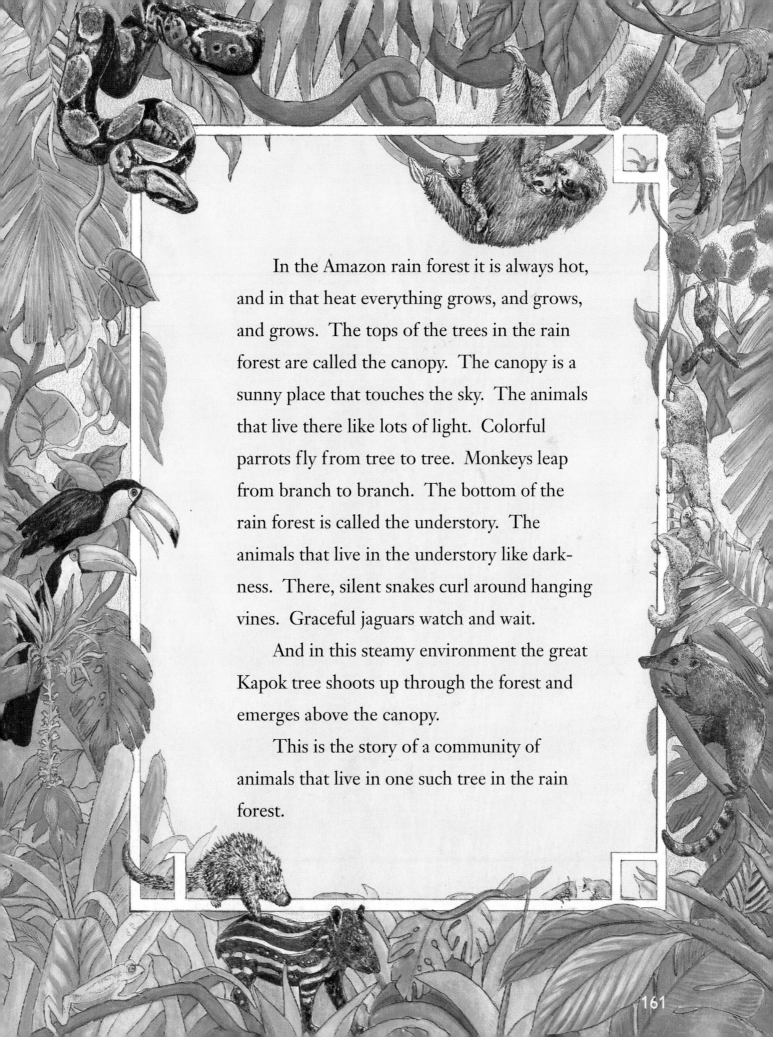

In the Amazon rain forest it is always hot, and in that heat everything grows, and grows, and grows. The tops of the trees in the rain forest are called the canopy. The canopy is a sunny place that touches the sky. The animals that live there like lots of light. Colorful parrots fly from tree to tree. Monkeys leap from branch to branch. The bottom of the rain forest is called the understory. The animals that live in the understory like darkness. There, silent snakes curl around hanging vines. Graceful jaguars watch and wait.

And in this steamy environment the great Kapok tree shoots up through the forest and emerges above the canopy.

This is the story of a community of animals that live in one such tree in the rain forest.

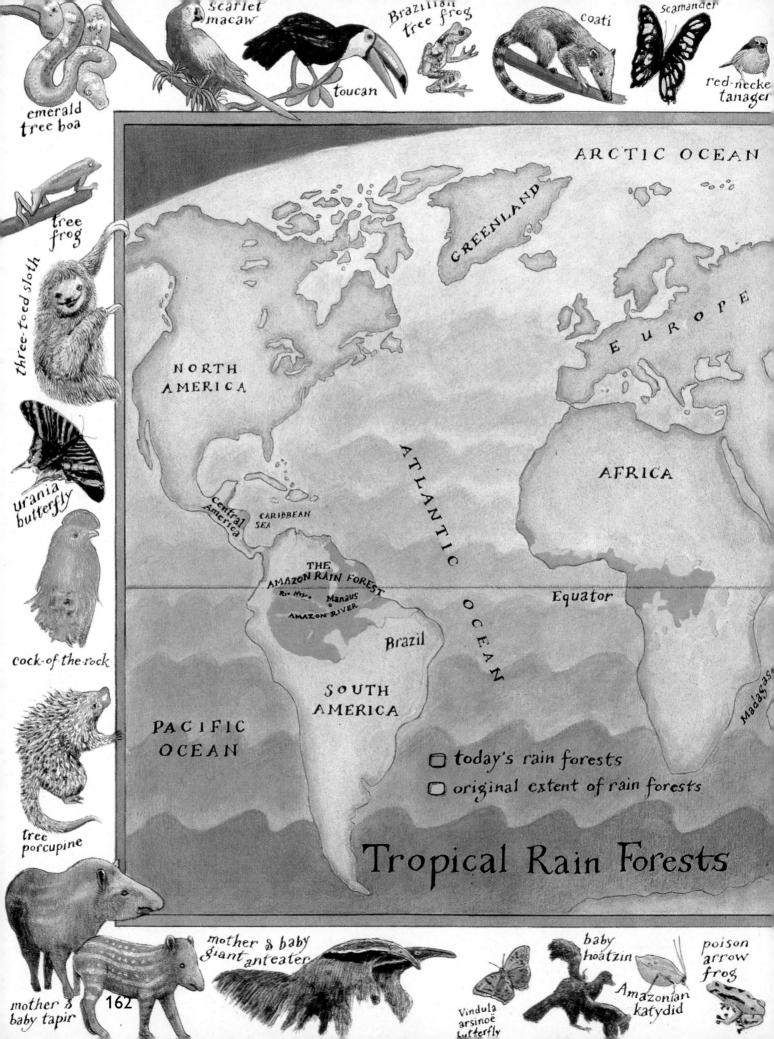

emerald
tree boa

tree
frog

three-toed sloth

urania
butterfly

cock-of-the-rock

tree
porcupine

mother &
baby tapir

scarlet
macaw

toucan

Brazilian
tree frog

coati

scamander

red-necke
tanager

ARCTIC OCEAN

GREENLAND

NORTH
AMERICA

EUROPE

AFRICA

Central
America

CARIBBEAN
SEA

ATLANTIC OCEAN

THE
AMAZON RAIN FOREST

Rio Negro   Manaus
AMAZON-RIVER

Equator

Brazil

Madagas

SOUTH
AMERICA

PACIFIC
OCEAN

□ today's rain forests
○ original extent of rain forests

Tropical Rain Forests

162

mother & baby
giant anteater

Vindula
arsinoë
butterfly

Amazonian
katydid

baby
hoatzin

poison
arrow
frog

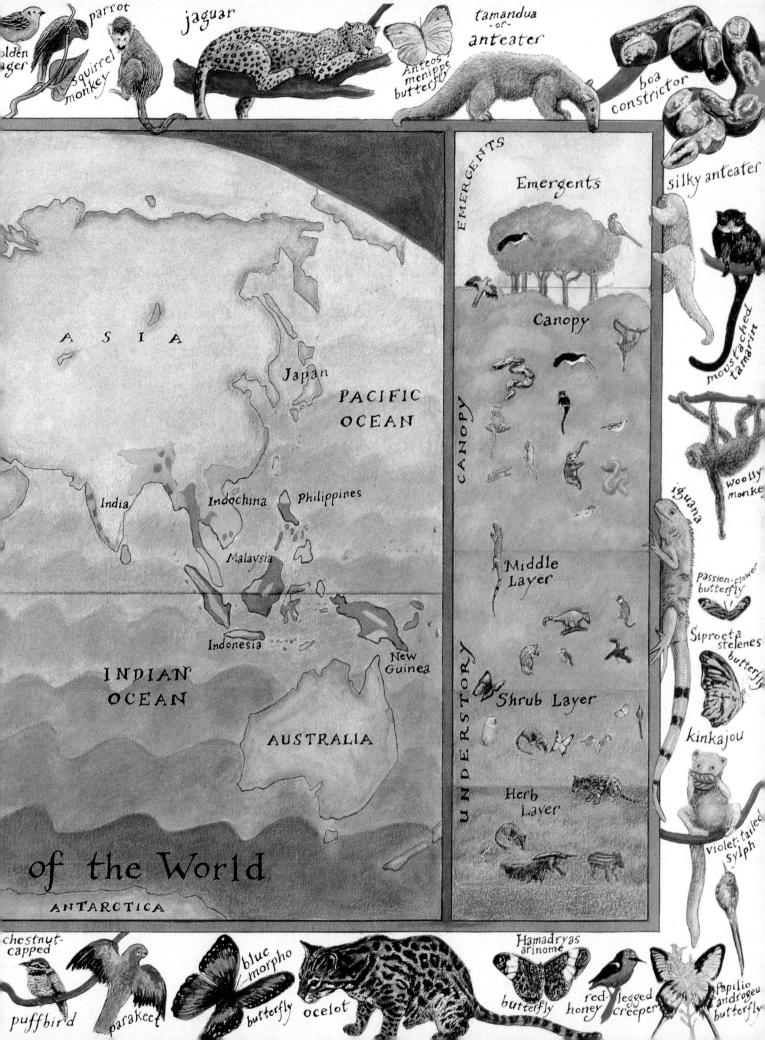

golden
~ager~

parrot

squirrel
monkey

jaguar

*Anteos
menippe
butterfly*

tamandua
~or~
anteater

boa
constrictor

silky anteater

moustached
tamarin

ASIA

Japan

PACIFIC
OCEAN

India

Indochina

Philippines

Malaysia

Indonesia

New
Guinea

INDIAN
OCEAN

AUSTRALIA

EMERGENTS

Emergents

Canopy

CANOPY

Middle
Layer

UNDERSTORY

Shrub Layer

Herb
Layer

woolly
monkey

iguana

passion-flower
butterfly

*Siproeta
stelenes
butterfly*

kinkajou

violet-tailed
sylph

of the World

ANTARCTICA

chestnut-
capped

puffbird

parakeet

blue
morpho
butterfly

ocelot

*Hamadryas
arinome*
butterfly

red-legged
honey
creeper

*Papilio
androgeu*
butterfly

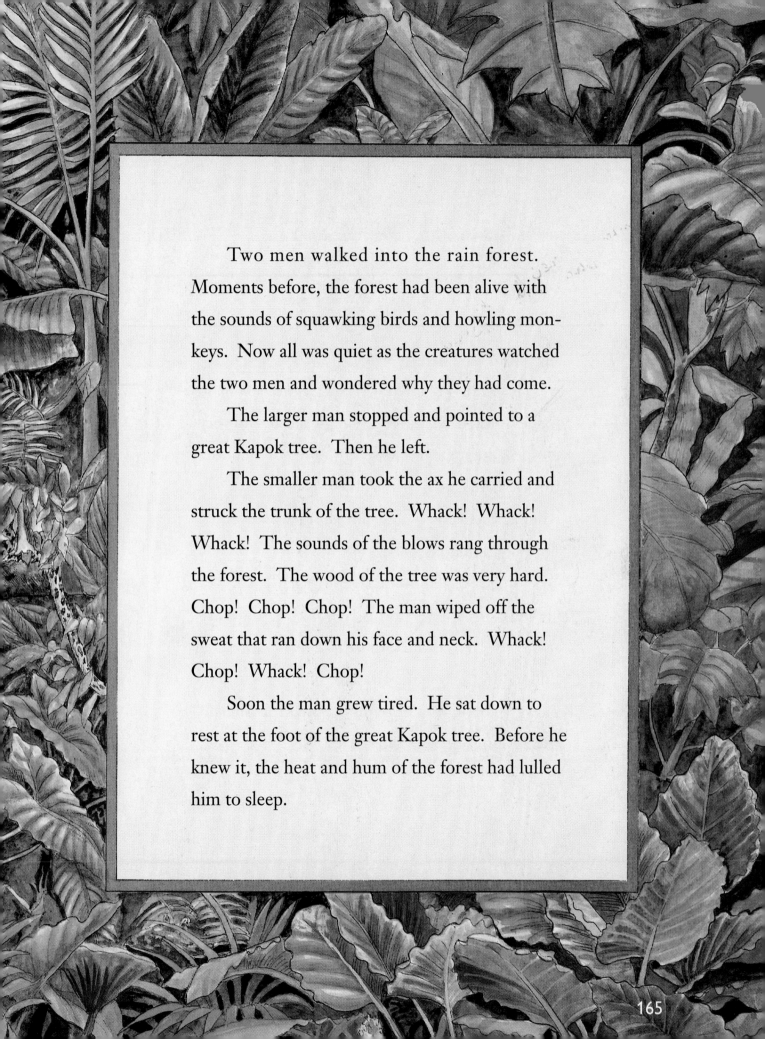

Two men walked into the rain forest. Moments before, the forest had been alive with the sounds of squawking birds and howling monkeys. Now all was quiet as the creatures watched the two men and wondered why they had come.

The larger man stopped and pointed to a great Kapok tree. Then he left.

The smaller man took the ax he carried and struck the trunk of the tree. Whack! Whack! Whack! The sounds of the blows rang through the forest. The wood of the tree was very hard. Chop! Chop! Chop! The man wiped off the sweat that ran down his face and neck. Whack! Chop! Whack! Chop!

Soon the man grew tired. He sat down to rest at the foot of the great Kapok tree. Before he knew it, the heat and hum of the forest had lulled him to sleep.

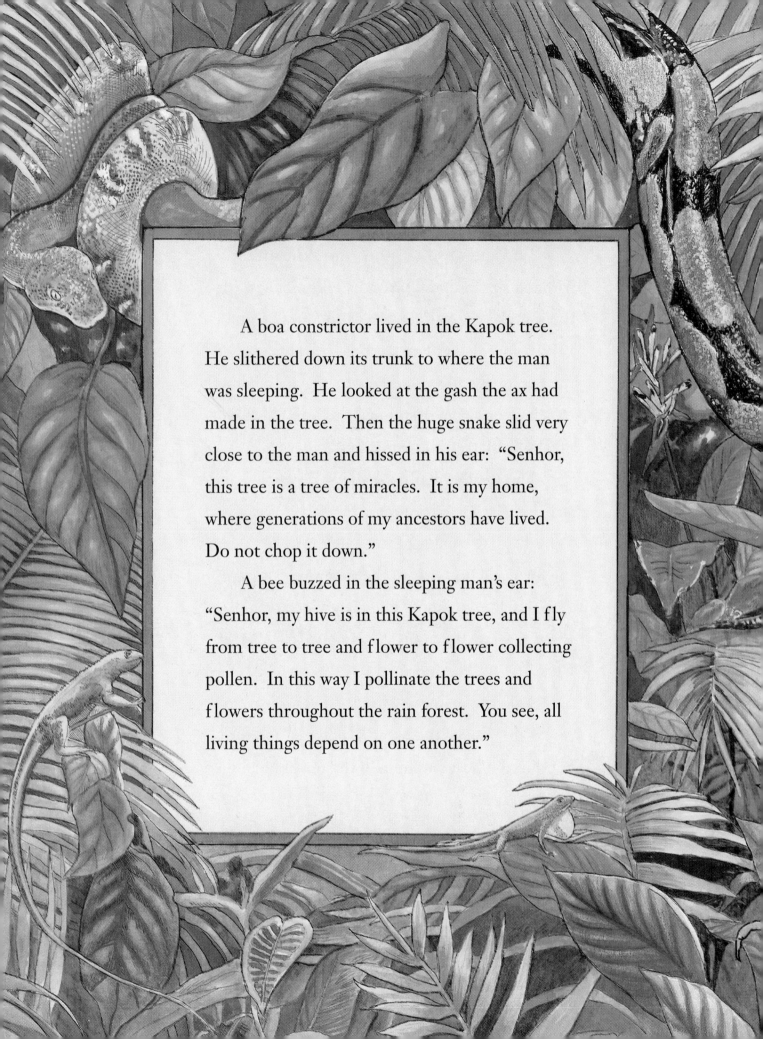

A boa constrictor lived in the Kapok tree.
He slithered down its trunk to where the man
was sleeping. He looked at the gash the ax had
made in the tree. Then the huge snake slid very
close to the man and hissed in his ear: "Senhor,
this tree is a tree of miracles. It is my home,
where generations of my ancestors have lived.
Do not chop it down."

A bee buzzed in the sleeping man's ear:
"Senhor, my hive is in this Kapok tree, and I fly
from tree to tree and flower to flower collecting
pollen. In this way I pollinate the trees and
flowers throughout the rain forest. You see, all
living things depend on one another."

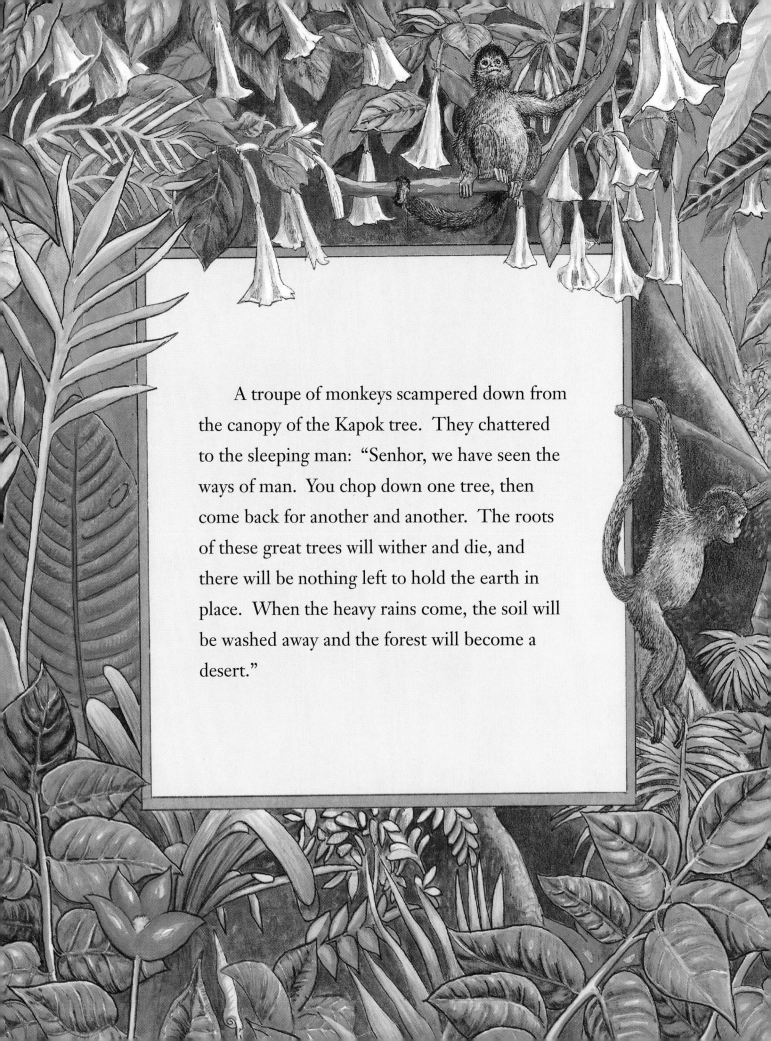

A troupe of monkeys scampered down from the canopy of the Kapok tree. They chattered to the sleeping man: "Senhor, we have seen the ways of man. You chop down one tree, then come back for another and another. The roots of these great trees will wither and die, and there will be nothing left to hold the earth in place. When the heavy rains come, the soil will be washed away and the forest will become a desert."

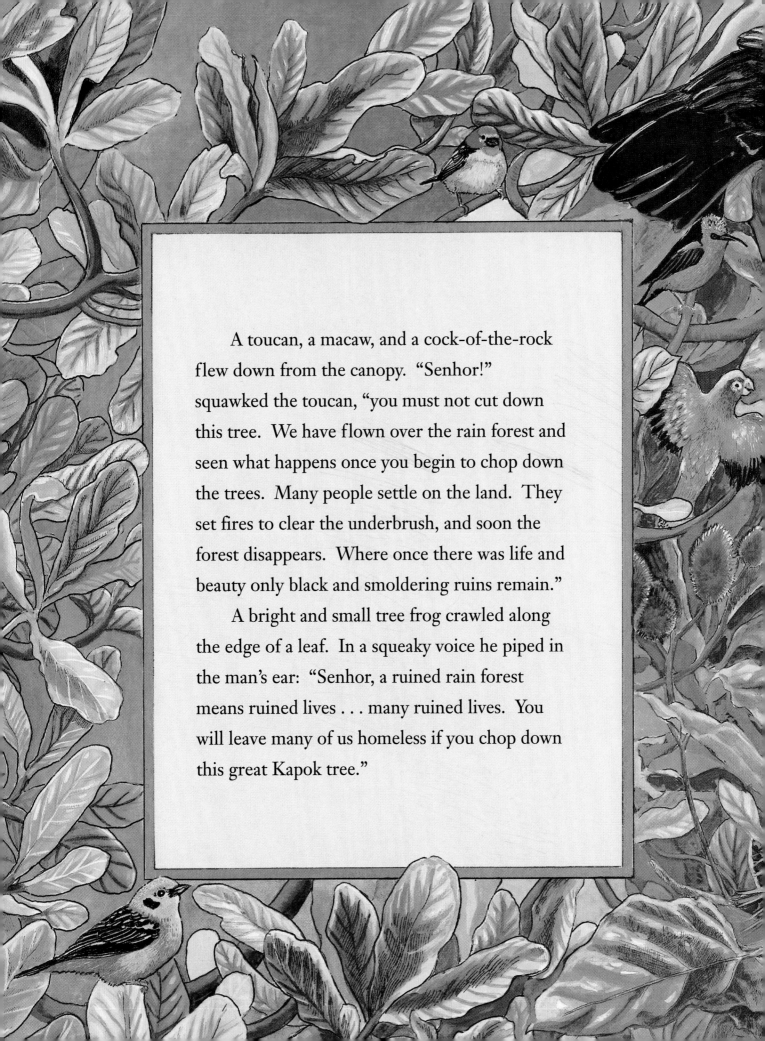

A toucan, a macaw, and a cock-of-the-rock flew down from the canopy. "Senhor!" squawked the toucan, "you must not cut down this tree. We have flown over the rain forest and seen what happens once you begin to chop down the trees. Many people settle on the land. They set fires to clear the underbrush, and soon the forest disappears. Where once there was life and beauty only black and smoldering ruins remain."

A bright and small tree frog crawled along the edge of a leaf. In a squeaky voice he piped in the man's ear: "Senhor, a ruined rain forest means ruined lives . . . many ruined lives. You will leave many of us homeless if you chop down this great Kapok tree."

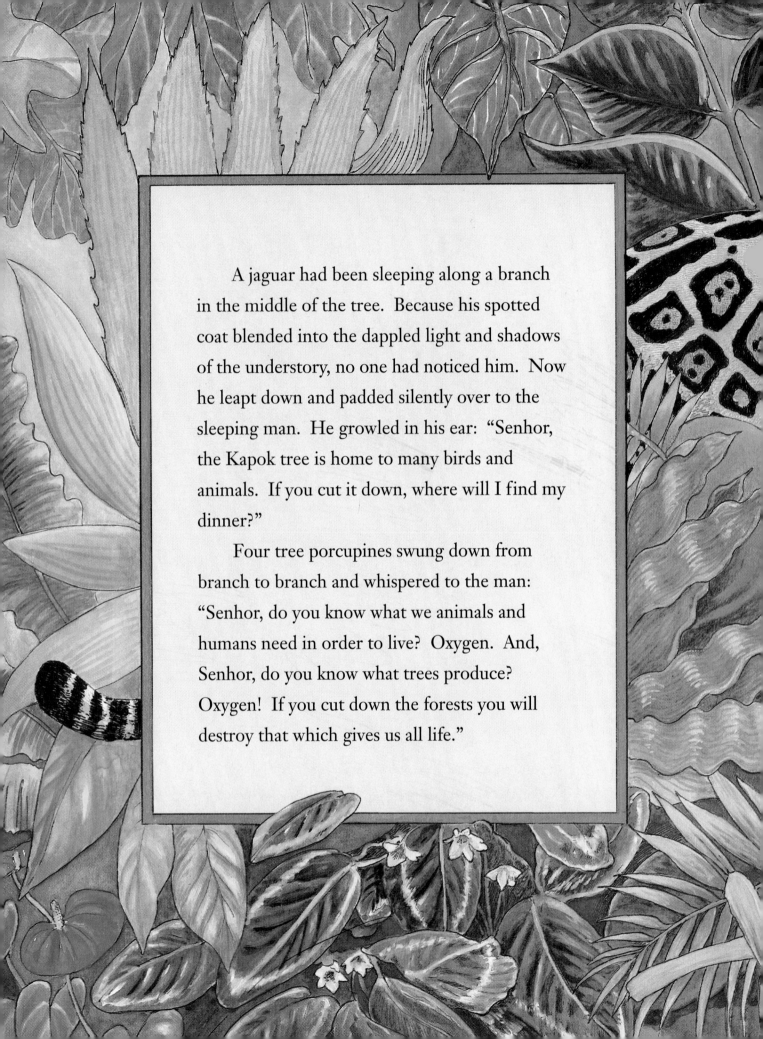

A jaguar had been sleeping along a branch in the middle of the tree. Because his spotted coat blended into the dappled light and shadows of the understory, no one had noticed him. Now he leapt down and padded silently over to the sleeping man. He growled in his ear: "Senhor, the Kapok tree is home to many birds and animals. If you cut it down, where will I find my dinner?"

Four tree porcupines swung down from branch to branch and whispered to the man: "Senhor, do you know what we animals and humans need in order to live? Oxygen. And, Senhor, do you know what trees produce? Oxygen! If you cut down the forests you will destroy that which gives us all life."

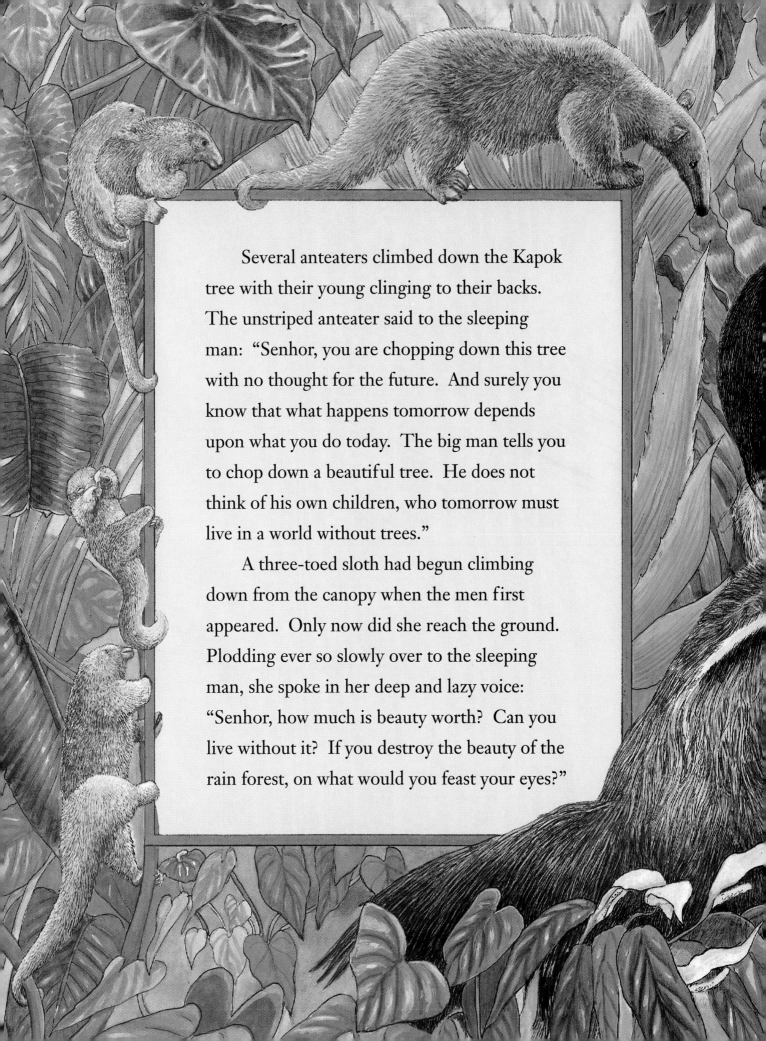

Several anteaters climbed down the Kapok tree with their young clinging to their backs. The unstriped anteater said to the sleeping man: "Senhor, you are chopping down this tree with no thought for the future. And surely you know that what happens tomorrow depends upon what you do today. The big man tells you to chop down a beautiful tree. He does not think of his own children, who tomorrow must live in a world without trees."

A three-toed sloth had begun climbing down from the canopy when the men first appeared. Only now did she reach the ground. Plodding ever so slowly over to the sleeping man, she spoke in her deep and lazy voice: "Senhor, how much is beauty worth? Can you live without it? If you destroy the beauty of the rain forest, on what would you feast your eyes?"

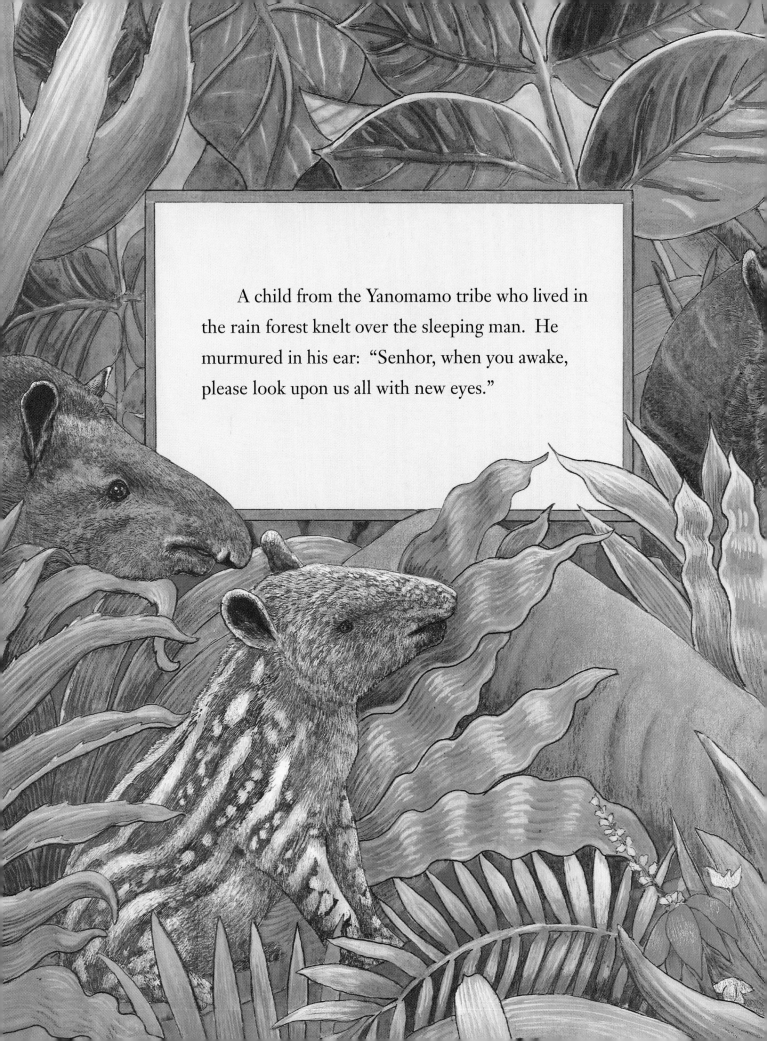

A child from the Yanomamo tribe who lived in the rain forest knelt over the sleeping man. He murmured in his ear: "Senhor, when you awake, please look upon us all with new eyes."

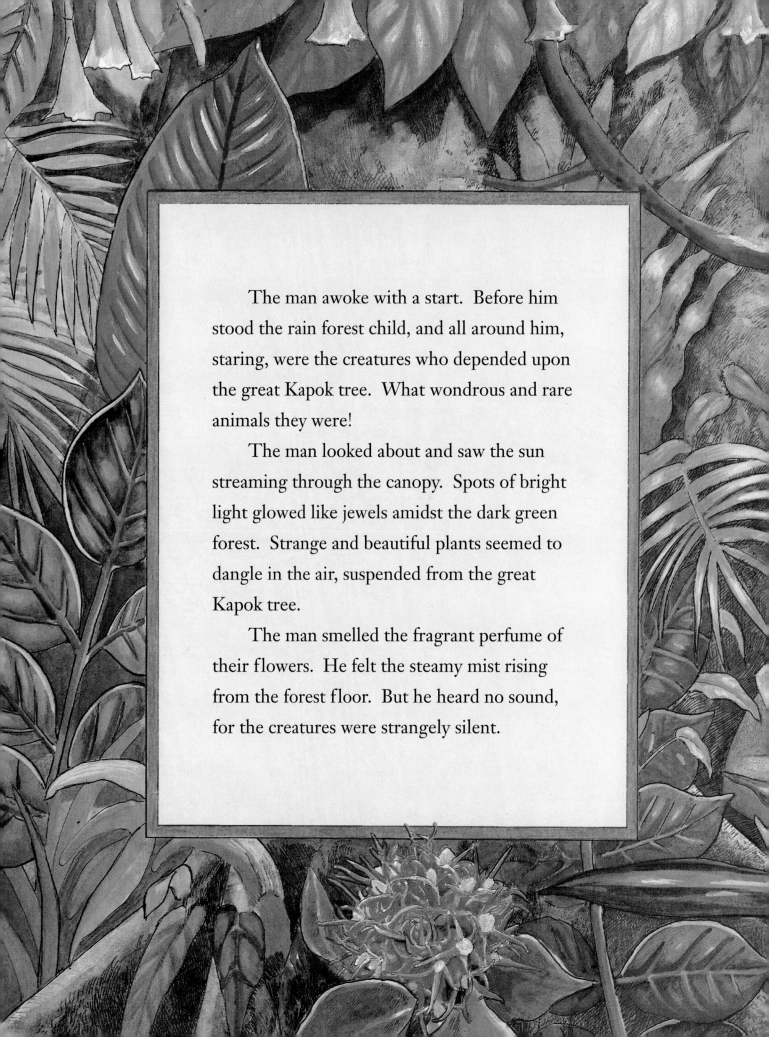

The man awoke with a start. Before him stood the rain forest child, and all around him, staring, were the creatures who depended upon the great Kapok tree. What wondrous and rare animals they were!

The man looked about and saw the sun streaming through the canopy. Spots of bright light glowed like jewels amidst the dark green forest. Strange and beautiful plants seemed to dangle in the air, suspended from the great Kapok tree.

The man smelled the fragrant perfume of their flowers. He felt the steamy mist rising from the forest floor. But he heard no sound, for the creatures were strangely silent.

The man stood and picked up his ax. He swung back his arm as though to strike the tree. Suddenly he stopped. He turned and looked at the animals and the child.

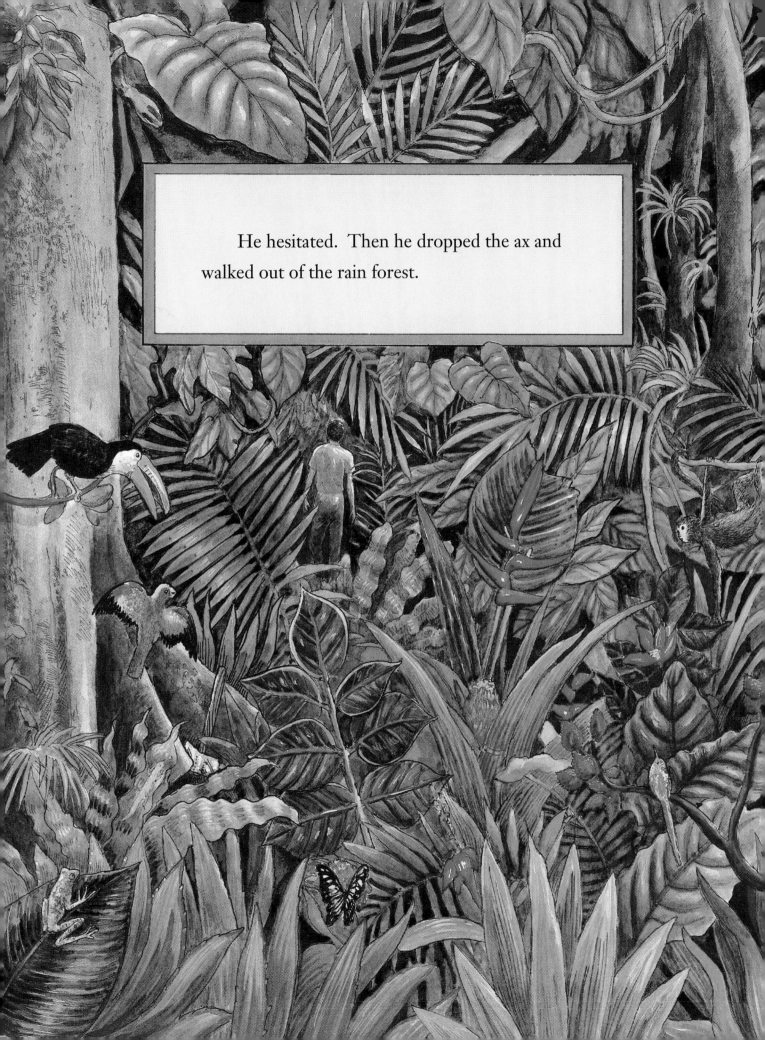

He hesitated. Then he dropped the ax and walked out of the rain forest.

Meet
LYNNE CHERRY

Lynne Cherry has strong feelings about preserving and protecting the environment. "Nature is the most beautiful thing in the world," she says. "That's why it kills me to see it destroyed, whether in this country or somewhere else."

She wrote *The Great Kapok Tree* to spread the alarm about the endangered Amazon rain forest. To prepare for her work on *The Great Kapok Tree,* Cherry visited the Amazon rain forest in Brazil to study the animals that live there and the plants that grow there. She wanted her drawings to be as accurate as possible.

Cherry continues to work hard to make people more aware of our fragile environment. Her book *A River Ran Wild* tells the true story of the troubled Nashua River in Massachusetts.

SPREAD

ACT OUT THE STORY

Buzz Like a Bee! Slither Like a Snake!

Perform *The Great Kapok Tree* with a group of class-mates. Each person can play a character from the story. Remember that each animal and the boy have special messages, and unique ways of delivering the messages to the man. Rehearse your play, and then perform it for the rest of your class.

MAKE A POSTER

"Preserve and Protect"

Spread the word! Pick one of the animals' messages to the man and turn it into a "Preserve and Protect" poster to help save the rain forest. Summarize the message as a slogan. Then make a poster featuring the animal and its slogan.

WRITE A PARAGRAPH

"Boy, Was I . . ."

How do you think the man felt when he woke up surrounded by all those animals? What thoughts went through his mind? Write a paragraph that describes what the man might have been thinking.

COMPARE AND CONTRAST

Two Forests

You've "visited" two forests — the rain forest in *The Great Kapok Tree* and the forest in *The Great Yellowstone Fire*. How are the forests similar? How are they different? Using the illustrations and photos to help you, write a compare-contrast paragraph or hold a discussion with your partner or a group.

Where Will the Waste Stop?

A Persuasive Essay by Megan Hunter

Megan had some ideas for solving a problem that she saw in her town. She wrote this essay to persuade other people to help.

**Megan Hunter
Washington Elementary School
Fargo, North Dakota**

"I like to write because it is fun, and it is a good way to express your thoughts without talking," said Megan. "I like to talk — don't get me wrong — but writing is just as great!" Megan wrote this essay when she was in the fourth grade.

In addition to writing, Megan likes to sing, act, swim, and read. She also enjoys downhill skiing, watching movies, and spending time with her family, friends, and pets.

186

Where Will the Waste Stop?

Landfills are a big problem. As I was riding in the car, I saw trash blowing, but not just anywhere. It was blowing outside of the landfill. It just blows out of the landfill and litters the places around it.

Even for a town like mine with 75,000 people in it, landfills are filling fast. Of the 180 acres of landfill space we have, 40 acres are being used. It is expected to be too full to hold trash in 25 to 30 years.

It makes me ashamed of my city, especially when I think that I live in a clean town. How can we attract visitors to our town when one of the borders is a dirty landfill?

I feel that something needs to be done before our city is completely bordered by trash. The things we can do to help are numerous. Here are three of them. One: Call the city government and ask about building fences around the landfill. Two: Recycle. The less trash there is, the less trash there will be blowing around, and the slower the landfill will fill up. Three: Call the city government and remind them that some people do not recycle. Ask if the workers at the landfill would recycle everything that is recyclable. Then there will be more space in the landfill, and it will last longer.

Remember — if you put your mind to something, you can accomplish it.

ACT

NOW

Kids Making

A Difference

Kids all over are

working to save the

Earth. Here are four

examples from *3-2-1*

Contact magazine.

Hope for KOPE

Kids at the Hawthorne School in Salt Lake City, UT, started a club called KOPE — Kids Organized to Protect the Environment. For the last three years, they've been working to turn a polluted creek bed into a nature park.

Half hidden in trees, the creek was full of tires, cement blocks and trash. The kids named the place "Hidden Hollow" and decided to clean it up. At the first clean-up event, 300 kids showed up to volunteer!

KOPE kids turned an old creek bed into a nature park.

"We wanted a place where kids can study plants in their natural environment," 10-year-old Tami Curtis told CONTACT.

The KOPE kids then learned that land developers had plans to turn the area into a parking lot. So they organized a "Hope for Hidden Hollow Conference." They invited kids from schools all across the city to help save the Hollow.

"We made a slide show to let people know what was happening," says Tami. She gave the developers a tour of the area to get them to change their minds. That didn't work.

But the KOPE kids didn't give up hope. They signed petitions, talked to local business people and went to city council meetings. And guess what? The council agreed to turn the area into a park! This spring, the kids will help plant shrubs, trees and flowers in the three-acre nature park.

"We didn't give up because we wanted a better place to live," says Tami. "I think our work shows other kids that they can make a difference."

Dynamic Duo

Rebecca and Phillippa Herbert of West Covina, CA, have also done tons for their neighborhood.

The two sisters discovered that many of their neighbors weren't recycling their trash. People thought it was a hassle to take the garbage to a local recycling center.

"So we thought, 'What if we start a recycling center in our front yard?'" Rebecca says. "That way, it would be easy for people to recycle."

Rebecca, 11, and Phillippa, 13, handed out information flyers in their neighborhood. The flyer said "Please help us recycle and save the Earth." It told when their center would be open. And it included tips on how to separate trash.

"We got cardboard boxes and labeled them Glass, Newspapers and Metals," Phillippa explains. "Every Saturday, we sat by the boxes and waited for people to drop off their trash."

The girls would then bring the boxes to a local recycling center. But they don't recycle trash in their front yard anymore. Their neighbors now do it on their own. Thanks to the girls, people recycle tons of stuff that otherwise would end up in landfills.

What's Up?

Kids at the Upper Bucks Vocational Technical School in Pennsylvania believe in kid power, too. They're building an 85-foot-tall windmill — right in front of their school!

The kids have high hopes for the windmill. They say it will produce enough electricity to power the electronic billboard in their school cafeteria, as well as their school radio station!

They also plan to use solar energy to help the windmill produce even more power. "We're going to put up the solar panels at the base of the windmill," says Jason Overholt. He's one of the student builders. "That way, we can also power the lights in our parking lot."

The windmill will save lots of energy, Jason told CONTACT. "Plus, windmills don't pollute the environment."

Kids in Pennsylvania have high hopes for the windmill they're building.

Melanie Essary speaks out against air pollution at a Senate hearing.

S.T.O.P. Starts

Lots of kids are pollution busters. Just ask Russell Essary, 11, of Forest Hills, NY. He and his younger sister Melanie have about 12,000 kids across the U.S. helping them solve pollution problems. They're all members of KiDS S.T.O.P.

Russell first started KiDS S.T.O.P. to battle the shrinking of the ozone layer. (The ozone layer is an invisible shield that protects Earth from the sun's harmful ultraviolet rays.)

Russell found out that the coolant in air conditioners is made of chemicals called CFCs. CFCs destroy the ozone layer. So KiDS S.T.O.P. got to work. They helped get a state law passed. Now all air conditioning fluid must be recycled. (That way, CFCs aren't released into the air.)

When Senator Al Gore (he's now Vice President) heard about the state law, he wrote to KiDS S.T.O.P. "He wanted to make it a national law," Russell says. And that's what happened. It's part of the 1990 Clean Air Act. Better still, CFCs will soon no longer be used.

There's no stopping the eco-kids. As Melanie told CONTACT, "If kids don't save the Earth, who will?"

from an article by Wendy Williams

190

Dream a Better World

**A clean, healthy environment is possible.
It starts with a dream . . . .**

I like to imagine what it would be like if we had no environmental problems. I imagine a beautiful world. The air is clean, there is no such thing as Styrofoam. I imagine I wake up in my own house, eat my usual foods. But while I'm walking to school, I realize that the air seems clean. In school, the water I wash my hands with is clean. When I ask my teacher about pollution, she says there is no such word. I also ask her about the Alaskan oil spill. She says there were never any oil spills. I can't believe it. I ask my friend to pinch me so I can wake up. Then I do wake up. But I want the world to be like my dream.

This was written by Gideon Javna, age nine.

I'm Gideon's uncle and I'm about to be a dad for the first time. I am very excited. But I wonder what the world will be like for my child. Will he or she be able to enjoy the beautiful blue sky and the sound of the ocean at the beach? . . . Or be able to walk in the woods? . . . Or be able to listen to birds singing on a still day? I hope so. That is my dream.

Dreams are the way we decide what we want. We imagine something . . . and then we make it happen. It is an amazing part of being a human being.

So if you care about saving the Earth — and I know you do — then keep dreaming. Let your imagination show you which way to go. Dream a better world.

This was written by John Javna, age forty.

191

PRIDE IN THE

Many American cities suffer from overcrowding, pollution, and too much garbage. But the young people of City Year are working to change all that.

City Year members are between seventeen and twenty-three years old and are from all different backgrounds. They take pride in working to make their cities better places to live.

City Year members work at full-time jobs in community-service projects such as building houses for the homeless, teaching in schools, planting gardens, cleaning up parks and playgrounds, and helping senior citizens. It's hard work. But City Year members know at the end of each day that they have helped put a little pride back into the communities they serve.

Peggy Johnson of Boston, Massachusetts, joined City Year in 1994, after talking to friends who were already members. She was inspired. So she signed up.

"City Year helps you down the line," Peggy says. "If you want to go to college it helps you get into college. It opens a lot of doors for you."

CITY

CITY YEAR

Peggy gets up and takes the subway to Boston's City Hall Plaza to meet her City Year corps. "I leave my house at 7:30. I come here, and then I find out what we're going to do today."

"It's good because you get to meet people. For instance, there are people who have already gone to college and there are people who are taking a year off to come here."

Peggy and the corps do physical training to warm up — and wake up — before going to their projects. "We have to wear our City Year jackets, pants, sweaters, shirts, boots, and book bags," says Peggy.

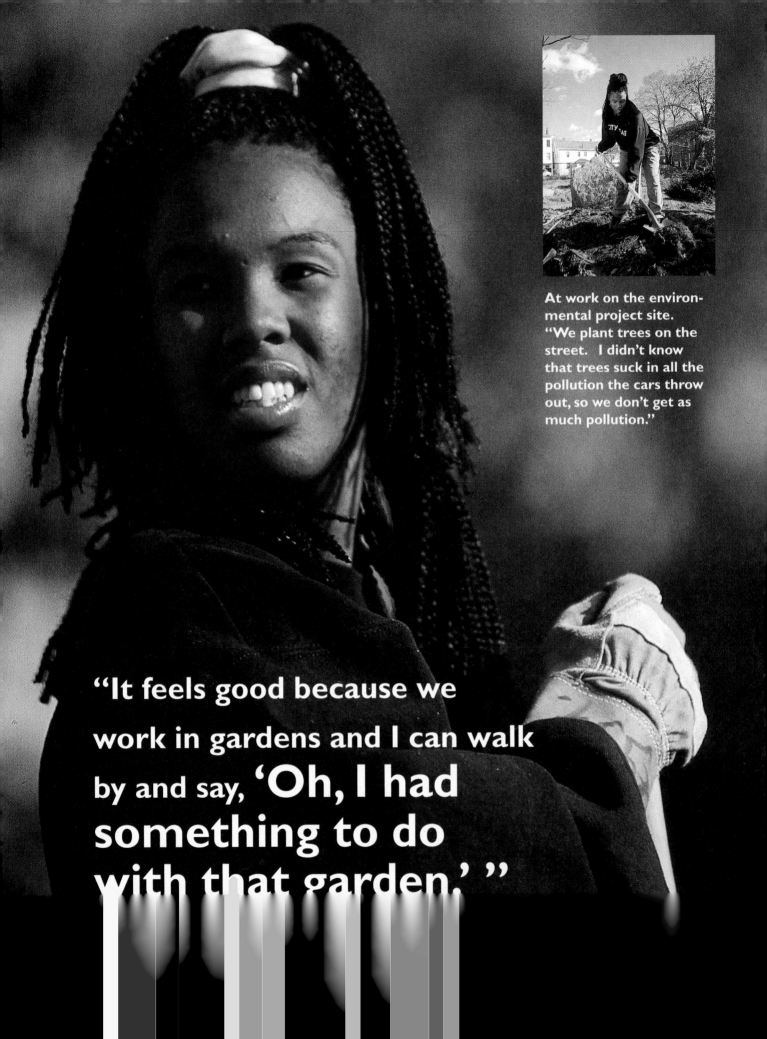

At work on the environmental project site. "We plant trees on the street. I didn't know that trees suck in all the pollution the cars throw out, so we don't get as much pollution."

"It feels good because we work in gardens and I can walk by and say, 'Oh, I had something to do with that garden.'"

Peggy on City Year: "Doing community service, that's what we do. That is what City Year's all about."

Peggy's team gets together for lunch.

City Year friends take a break. Peggy says that she has "always loved learning about other people's cultures."

At the end of a long, busy day, Peggy and her teammates are tired but happy.

Meet
Chris Van Allsburg

For Chris Van Allsburg, the author and illustrator of many award-winning books, words and pictures go together. But for *Just a Dream,* the words and pictures came together in an unusual way. Van Allsburg says that most of the time "A story starts with a picture in my mind .... If I have nothing to do, an idea comes. With *Just a Dream* it was different. I started with the idea of getting kids concerned about pollution .... The hard thing when you're writing about real things — like pollution — as opposed to fiction, is to write a good story."

The pictures he uses to illustrate this very good story show Van Allsburg's special way of imagining things. His pictures are full of surprises. He likes to put things where you don't expect to see them, such as a bed on top of a smokestack or in a tree. He often shows things from unusual points of view too, such as houses as they would look from the sky.

Van Allsburg says that when he reads a book, he imagines how the people and the places look. When he writes a book, he likes to leave the reader with something to imagine too. "I like turning a face away a little bit .... I also like leaving something out of the story. There must be something to ponder at the end."

Van Allsburg's first book, *The Garden of Abdul Gasazi,* told about a small white dog named Fritz. Since then, Fritz has become something of a trademark. If you look hard enough, you will find him somewhere in most of Van Allsburg's books. Can you find him in *Just a Dream?*

JUST A DREAM
STORY AND PICTURES BY CHRIS VAN ALLSBURG

    As usual, Walter stopped at the bakery on his way home from
school. He bought one large jelly-filled doughnut. He took the
pastry from its bag, eating quickly as he walked along. He licked
the red jelly from his fingers. Then he crumpled up the empty
bag and threw it at a fire hydrant.

At home Walter saw Rose, the little girl next door, watering a tree that had just been planted. "It's my birthday present," she said proudly. Walter couldn't understand why anyone would want a tree for a present. His own birthday was just a few days away, "And I'm not getting some dumb plant," he told Rose.

After dinner Walter took out the trash. Three cans stood
next to the garage. One was for bottles, one for cans, and one for
everything else. As usual, Walter dumped everything into one
can. He was too busy to sort through garbage, especially when
there was something good on television.

The show that Walter was so eager to watch was about a boy
who lived in the future. The boy flew around in a tiny airplane
that he parked on the roof of his house. He had a robot and a

small machine that could make any kind of food with the push of a button.

Walter went to bed wishing he lived in the future. He couldn't wait to have his own tiny plane, a robot to take out the trash, and a machine that could make jelly doughnuts by the thousands. When he fell asleep, his wish came true. That night Walter's bed traveled to . . . the future.

Walter woke up in the middle of a huge dump. A bulldozer was pushing a heap of bulging trash bags toward him. "Stop!" he yelled.

The man driving the bulldozer put his machine in neutral. "Oh, sorry," he said. "Didn't see you."

Walter looked at the distant mountains of trash and saw half-buried houses. "Do people live here?" he asked.

"Not anymore," answered the man.

A few feet from the bed was a rusty old street sign that read FLORAL AVENUE. "Oh no," gasped Walter. He lived on Floral Avenue.

The driver revved up his bulldozer. "Well," he shouted, "back to work!"

Walter pulled the covers over his head. This can't be the future, he thought. I'm sure it's just a dream. He went back to sleep.

But not for long . . .

Walter peered over the edge of his bed, which was caught in the branches of a tall tree. Down below, he could see two men carrying a large saw. "Hello!" Walter yelled out.

"Hello to you!" they shouted back.

"You aren't going to cut down this tree, are you?" Walter asked.

But the woodcutters didn't answer. They took off their jackets, rolled up their sleeves, and got to work. Back and forth they pushed the saw, slicing through the trunk of Walter's tree. "You must need this tree for something important," Walter called down.

"Oh yes," they said, "very important." Then Walter noticed lettering on the woodcutters' jackets. He could just make out the words: QUALITY TOOTHPICK COMPANY. Walter sighed and slid back under the blankets.

Until . . .

Walter couldn't stop coughing. His bed was balanced on the rim of a giant smokestack. The air was filled with smoke that burned his throat and made his eyes itch. All around him, dozens of smokestacks belched thick clouds of hot, foul smoke. A workman climbed one of the stacks.

"What is this place?" Walter called out.

"This is the Maximum Strength Medicine Factory," the man answered.

"Gosh," said Walter, looking at all the smoke, "what kind of medicine do they make here?"

"Wonderful medicine," the workman replied, "for burning throats and itchy eyes."

Walter started coughing again.

"I can get you some," the man offered.

"No thanks," said Walter. He buried his head in his pillow and, when his coughing stopped, fell asleep.

But then . . .

Snowflakes fell on Walter. He was high in the mountains. A group of people wearing snow-shoes and long fur coats hiked past his bed.

"Where are you going?" Walter asked.

"To the hotel," one of them replied.

Walter turned around and saw an enormous building. A sign on it read HOTEL EVEREST. "Is that hotel," asked Walter, "on the top of Mount Everest?"

"Yes," said one of the hikers. "Isn't it beautiful?"

"Well," Walter began. But the group didn't wait for his answer. They waved goodbye and marched away. Walter stared at the flashing yellow sign, then crawled back beneath his sheets.

But there was more to see . . .

Walter's hand was wet and cold. When he opened his eyes, he found himself floating on the open sea, drifting toward a fishing boat. The men on the boat were laughing and dancing.

"Ship ahoy!" Walter shouted.

The fishermen waved to him.

"What's the celebration for?" he asked.

"We've just caught a fish," one of them yelled back. "Our second one this week!" They held up their small fish for Walter to see.

"Aren't you supposed to throw the little ones back?" Walter asked.

But the fishermen didn't hear him. They were busy singing and dancing.

Walter turned away. Soon the rocking of the bed put him to sleep.

But only for a moment . . .

A loud, shrieking horn
nearly lifted Walter off his mat-
tress. He jumped up. There were
cars and trucks all around him,
horns honking loudly, creeping
along inch by inch. Every driver
had a car phone in one hand and a
big cup of coffee in the other.
When the traffic stopped completely, the honking grew even
louder. Walter could not get back
to sleep.

Hours passed, and he won-
dered if he'd be stuck on this
highway forever. He pulled his
pillow tightly around his head.
This can't be the future, he
thought. Where are the tiny airplanes, the robots? The honking
continued into the night, until
finally, one by one, the cars became quiet as their drivers, and
Walter, went to sleep.

But his bed traveled on . . .

Walter looked up. A horse stood right over his bed, staring directly at him. In the saddle was a woman wearing cowboy clothes. "My horse likes you," she said.

"Good," replied Walter, who wondered where he'd ended up this time. All he could see was a dull yellow haze.

"Son," the woman told him, spreading her arms in front of her, "this is the mighty Grand Canyon."

Walter gazed into the foggy distance.

"Of course," she went on, "with all this smog, nobody's gotten a good look at it for years." The woman offered to sell Walter some postcards that showed the canyon in the old days. "They're real pretty," she said.

But he couldn't look. It's just a dream, he told himself. I know I'll wake up soon, back in my room.

But he didn't . . .

216

Walter looked out from under his sheets. His bed was flying through the night sky. A flock of ducks passed overhead. One of them landed on the bed, and to Walter's surprise, he began to speak. "I hope you don't mind," the bird said, "if I take a short rest here." The ducks had been flying for days, looking for the pond where they had always stopped to eat.

"I'm sure it's down there somewhere," Walter said, though he suspected something awful might have happened. After a while the duck waddled to the edge of the bed, took a deep breath, and flew off. "Good luck," Walter called to him. Then he pulled the blanket over his head. "It's just a dream," he whispered, and wondered if it would ever end.

Then finally . . .

Walter's bed returned to the present. He was safe in his room again, but he felt terrible. The future he'd seen was not what he'd expected. Robots and little airplanes didn't seem very important now. He looked out his window at the trees and lawns in the early morning light, then jumped out of bed.

218

He ran outside and down the block, still in his pajamas. He
found the empty jelly doughnut bag he'd thrown at the fire hydrant the day before. Then Walter went back home and, before
the sun came up, sorted all the trash by the garage.

A few days later, on Walter's birthday, all his friends came
over for cake and ice cream. They loved his new toys: the
laser gun set, electric yo-yo, and inflatable dinosaurs. "My best
present," Walter told them, "is outside." Then he showed them
the gift that he'd picked out that morning — a tree.

After the party, Walter and his dad planted the birthday present. When he went to bed, Walter looked out his window. He could see his tree and the tree Rose had planted on her birthday. He liked the way they looked, side by side. Then he went to sleep, but not for long, because that night Walter's bed took him away again.

When Walter woke up, his bed was standing in the shade of two tall trees. The sky was blue. Laundry hanging from a clothesline flapped in the breeze. A man pushed an old motorless lawn mower. This isn't the future, Walter thought. It's the past.

"Good morning," the man said. "You've found a nice place to sleep."

"Yes, I have," Walter agreed. There was something very peaceful about the huge trees next to his bed.

The man looked up at the rustling leaves. "My great-grandmother planted one of these trees," he said, "when she was a little girl."

Walter looked up at the leaves too, and realized where his bed had taken him. This was the future, after all, a different kind of future. There were still no robots or tiny airplanes. There weren't even any clothes dryers or gas-powered lawn mowers. Walter lay back and smiled. "I like it here," he told the man, then drifted off to sleep in the shade of the two giant trees — the trees he and Rose had planted so many years ago.

Dream On

Best of All

"So, Walter, your favorite birthday present is . . . a tree?" How do you think Walter would explain that? Write a letter from Walter to a friend or relative. Include Walter's feelings about all the birthday presents he got in *Just a Dream* and why he likes the tree best.

Perform a Scene

On Stage

Bring one of Walter's dreams to life. Work with one or two classmates to choose a dream scene and to decide who will play each part. Add some action and dialogue to the scene, and then present it to your class.

What a Chore!

Think about Walter's household chores and how he felt about them. Do you feel about your chores the way Walter felt at the beginning of the story or more like what he felt at the end? What would happen if you didn't do your chores? What if no one in the world did those particular chores? Respond with a poem, story, or drawing.

Wake-up Call

Walter sure learns a lot in his sleep! After thinking about how Walter changes in *Just a Dream*, look back at *The Great Kapok Tree*. How are the two stories similar? How are they different? Write about your ideas or discuss them with a classmate or your group.

225

Acknowledgments

"Birdfoot's Grampa," by Joseph Bruchac, from *Entering Onondaga.* Copyright © 1978 by Joseph Bruchac. Reprinted by permission of Barbara S. Kouts for the author.

"Earth Day Kids," from April 1993 *3-2-1 Contact* magazine. Copyright © 1993 by Children's Television Workshop. Reprinted by permission.

Excerpt from *50 Simple Things Kids Can Do to Save the Earth,* by John Javna. Copyright © 1990 by John Javna. Reprinted by permission of Universal Press Syndicate.

"Gluscabi and the Wind Eagle," told by Joseph Bruchac, from *Native American Stories,* by Joseph Bruchac and Michael J. Caduto. Copyright © 1991 by Joseph Bruchac. Reprinted by permission of Fulcrum Publishing.

The Great Kapok Tree, by Lynne Cherry. Copyright © 1990 by Lynne Cherry. Reprinted by permission of Harcourt Brace & Company.

The Great Yellowstone Fire, by Carole Vogel. Copyright © 1990 by Carole Vogel and Kathryn Goldner. Reprinted by permission of Little, Brown and Company.

Just a Dream, by Chris Van Allsburg. Copyright © 1990 by Chris Van Allsburg. Reprinted by permission of Houghton Mifflin Company. All rights reserved.

"Smoke Jumpers," by Janice Koch, from *National Geographic World,* August 1994. Copyright © 1994 by the National Geographic Society. Reprinted by permission of *National Geographic World,* the official magazine for Junior Members of the National Geographic Society.

"We Are Plooters," by Jack Prelutsky, illustrated by Paul O. Zelinsky, from *The Big Book for Our Planet,* edited by Ann Durell, Jean Craighead George, and Katherine Paterson, published by Penguin USA. Text copyright © 1993 by Jack Prelutsky. Reprinted by permission of the author. Illustrations copyright © 1993 by Paul O. Zelinsky. Reprinted by permission of the artist.

Credits

Illustration   **146–155** Lark Carrier;   **161–183** Lynne Cherry;   **197–223** Chris Van Allsburg;   **158–159** Paul Zelinsky

Assignment Photography   **192, 193, 194, 195** Kindra Clineff;   **80–81, 91–92, 146–155, 184, 188–189** Tony Scarpetta;   **114–115, 116, 117–118, 224–225** Tracey Wheeler

Photography   **2** KOPE;   **3** Dan Church/Intelligencer; **120** © Jerry L. Ferrara/Photo Researchers, Inc.;   **121** Robert Bower;   **124** B.I.F.C.;   **126** Yellowstone National Park;   **128** ©Alan and Sandy Carey;   **129** © Jeff and Alexa Henry;   **131** Yellowstone National Park;   **136** Steven Dowell/Bozeman Chronicle;   **141** Courtesy of Carole Vogel;   **141** Courtesy of Kathryn Goldner;   **144** (cover) Daniel R. Westergren © National Geographic Society;   **144** © Bill Moyer 1992 (inset);   **144** Michael S. Yamashita;   **145** Bill Moyer © National Geographic Society;   **183** Katie MacManus, *Teaching K–8* magazine; **184–185** Gary Lewis/The Stock Market;   **194** Susan Lapides